The Steve Knightley Songbook

Dave Mallinson Publications & **Isis Publishing**

The Steve Knightley Songbook
© 1996 Isis Publishing and Dave Mallinson Publications

First produced and published in England in 1996 by Dave Mallinson Publications
3 East View, Moorside, Cleckheaton, West Yorkshire, England BD19 6LD
Telephone: 01274 876388, facsimile: 01274 865208, e-mail: mally@jorum.demon.co.uk

ISBN 1 899512 34 9

British Library Cataloguing in Publication Data
A catalogue record for this book is available from the British Library

Text set in Galileo; music engraved in Petrucci using *Finale*; page layout in *QuarkXPress*

Data capture, manipulation and layout by David J Taylor

Original cover concept and design by Stylorouge, London, telephone 0171 229 9131
Printed by RAP Limited, Rochdale, telephone 01706 44981

Contents

The Steve Knightley Songbook

Introduction

STEVE KNIGHTLEY'S career, an object lesson in perseverance, has produced a body of work that dominates the repertoire of *Show of Hands*, the duo he and Phil Beer formed in 1987. His background, he has said, provides all the ingredients for an itinerant, West Country, Celtic story-teller...

> *I was born in Southampton in 1954. My mother's grandfather was dockmaster and there are dark family rumours that one of his ancestors was a Polish, or possibly Jewish, sailor, who came ashore whilst sick and married a local girl. My own grandfathers, who died before I was born, also worked in the docks after their army service; one was a career soldier in the Dorset Regiment, the other fought with the Hampshire Regiment. My grandmothers were Irish and Scottish, one from Limavady and the other from Annan in the Borders. My father initially worked as a fireman in Southampton but he and my mother found work with the Social Services as foster parents in boys' homes. We moved house a lot, to Ledbury in Herefordshire, to Portsmouth; then, when I was five, we settled in East Devon where I was really brought up. Dad managed a television shop, worked in a café, drove taxis...anything to make a living, really. I went to school in Exeter and Exmouth and I began singing and playing guitar at the age of 14.*

Knightley was first attracted to acoustic music after hearing some Joan Baez albums belonging to his step-brother, a soldier. However, when he later heard *The Freewheelin' Bob Dylan* album, he recognised that much of the music he had been learning as a teenager was firmly rooted in the English and Celtic traditions. On the sleeve of the Dylan record, Martin Carthy's name is mentioned:

> *When I was 15, I saw Carthy and Swarbrick at Sidmouth. I realised that what appealed about Dylan and Baez were the British roots of their material. I bought a copy of **Prince Heathen** and for the next few years was seriously into traditional music.*

Apart from Dylan, American songwriters didn't interest him, although he was drawn to the sound and texture of American acoustic instruments:

> *When I started writing, it was natural that I should draw upon English themes and use British melodic and narrative idioms.*

Whilst still at school in Exmouth, he formed the group *Gawain* with guitarist Paul Downes and fiddler 'Bat' Evans. Together they played in folk clubs and bars throughout East Devon. The trio disbanded in 1973 and Knightley left home to study politics and history in Coventry. Although he had begun to write his own songs, he was known more as a singer of traditional material. Meanwhile, Downes had teamed up with another Devonian musician, Phil Beer. Both Downes and Beer regularly stayed with Knightley whenever they were working in the Midlands. They also began to include some of his songs in their live shows.

In the late '70s, Knightley moved to Brighton and took a postgraduate certificate in education at Sussex University. He began performing with Paul's brother, Warwick, a double bass player and they enjoyed two years of local success. In 1979, he swapped his acoustic guitar for a Fender electric guitar and moved to London. His bands *Short Stories*, *The Cheats* and *Total Strangers* all played on the pub rock circuit from '79 to '85, drawing an enthusiastic following at venues such as the Golden Lion and the Half Moon. Knightley also had to make use of his teaching qualifications in order to earn enough to survive:

> *I taught guitar at Quentin Kynaston school, a fairly tough comprehensive in Swiss Cottage. After a while I was asked to do some supply work. So with long hair and leather jacket, I spent a week covering for the deputy head, wandering around with a clipboard asking kids where they were supposed to be.*

At various times during this period, when *Short Stories* band members were unavailable, Phil Beer would stand in on lead guitar and Knightley occasionally returned the favour by playing bass in *Arizona Smoke Revue*, a group which included Beer, Downes, and Americans Pete and Bill Zorn. Loosely based on David Bromberg's big band—lots of singers playing lots of instruments—this group made three albums and enjoyed some cult status without crossing over into the mainstream. For contractual reasons when he appeared with this combo, Knightley adopted the pseudonym of 'Gene Vogel'!

Accepting in '85 that his rock bands were unlikely to achieve genuine success, Knightley moved back to the West Country and settled in rural Dorset with his wife Simone, a designer. There they opened a remote country guest house. Meanwhile, the **Arizonas** had split up and Phil was invited to join the **Albion Band**. Steve and Phil met up again at the Wimborne Festival in '86, where Steve, playing with Warwick Downes and Martin Bradley, performed a set using the name **Show of Hands**. This trio was short-lived, but Beer and Knightley had reconnected. Together they bought an 8-track recorder which was installed in a barn behind the guest house in Corscombe and when **Albion Band** commitments allowed, they began work on what eventually became the first **Show of Hands** cassette.

As well as running the guest house and giving occasional performances with Phil Beer, Knightley began to utilise his academic qualifications:

> *I started giving guitar lessons and was in demand as a supply teacher at the local comprehensive school in Beaminster. One student was Polly (P.J.) Harvey, whose father, a stonemason, supplied us with stone and topsoil in exchange for guitar lessons. We played together once at our local village fête with Polly on saxophone...I think her mother may still have the photos!*

Beer left the **Albion Band** in '91 and **Show of Hands** began in earnest. With the help of their agent, Peter Wilson, they spent two years playing in pubs, clubs and bars throughout the south-west, finally breaking into the concert and festival scene in '93. Knightley continued work as a part-time teacher (media studies, music and history) until 1994, when **Show of Hands** became his full-time occupation. The duo's repertoire, which at first had consisted of standards, folk songs and Knightley originals, was now dominated by Steve's compositions, although they always included some traditional music in their set:

> *Some people have assumed that **Tall Ships** or **The Galway Farmer** are traditional songs—I always take that as a real compliment.*

KNIGHTLEY and Beer, as well as playing as **Show of Hands**, have worked with exiled Chilean musicians, Vladimir Vega, Sergio Avila and Mauricio Venegas, who together with English melodeon player Dave Townsend, formed **Alianza**. This group was the brainchild of Roger Watson of Bracknell based **TAPS**, or Traditional Arts Projects. Knightley feels that the experience of playing in this sextet was enormously valuable:

> *Working with people who have been mistreated, imprisoned or exiled because they played music makes you realise what power music can have. It made me reappraise what I was doing and also reflect on the whole acoustic/folk genre: songs can contain truths and sentiments that can inform as well as entertain. In places such as Ireland and South America, where traditional music still lives, musicians instinctively know this, but English musicians don't often necessarily acquire this perspective. Both playing original songs in pubs and working with **Alianza** has given me a broader perspective towards both my material and the audience.*

So which other singers or songwriters does Knightley respect today?

> *It's hard for me to pick up an acoustic guitar without being aware of the shadows of Bob Dylan and Martin Carthy. I return to songs like **Girl From The North Country** and **Seven Yellow Gypsies** again and again. I also like the irony and particular Englishness of Jethro Tull's Ian Anderson.*

How does he describe his songs?

> *I try to combine the narrative and melodic strengths of the English and Celtic traditions with textures and rhythms from North and South America. That sounds a bit complicated, I know...but really I'm just a story-teller, trying to tell stories.*

John Tobler, Folk Roots, London 1995.

Ah So!

Words and music by Steve Knightley
From 'Backlog 1987-1991'

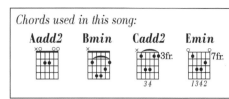

Chords used in this song:
Aadd2   Bmin   Cadd2   Emin

Andante ♩ = 100

Intro

Emin *(1st verse 8vb)*

Nis- san mak - ing mo - tors in _____ the far north - east,

Throw a - way your cards, _____ you can join the feast,

We work day and night, we all play the game,

We meet ev- 'ry morn _____ ing and we look the same and

Cadd2   Bmin

drive   a com- p'ny car, _____ watch him go! _____

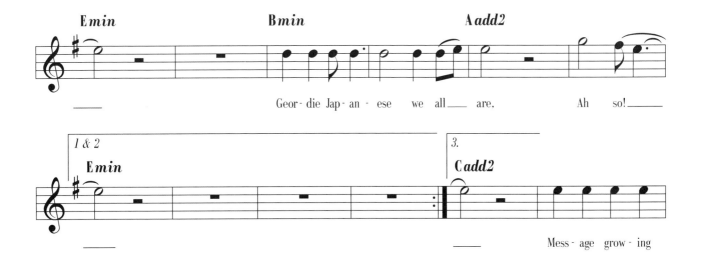

Geor-die Jap-an-ese we all—— are, Ah so!——

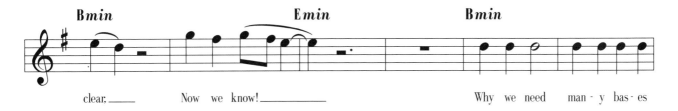

—— Mess-age grow-ing

clear,—— Now we know!—————— Why we need man-y bas-es

here,——————— Ah so!———————————— Oh

no!———— Oh Ah! Ah!

2.
I see they're sitting pretty by the deep, dark Rhine,
Made a few mistakes 'n' got it right this time,
No more waving flags, marching up and down,
Sit behind the wheel, watch the world go 'round,
And each machine built to last, watch it go!
Don't ever talk about the past, oh no!

3.
There's a nasty rumour that's been going 'round,
Now they've found the way to make this country sound,
One way to revive, one sure way to wealth,
Ruin our big cities and then wreck our health,
But first you need a volunteer to aim the blow,
Every day we all live in fear, ah no!

All Your Fault

Words and music by Steve Knightley
From 'Show of Hands Live'

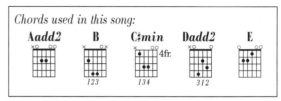

I woke to-day___ I heard the rain com-ing in, My head too hea___vy and my

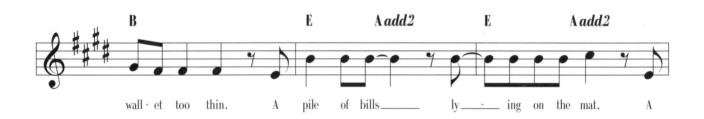

wall-et too thin, A pile of bills_____ ly___ing on the mat, A

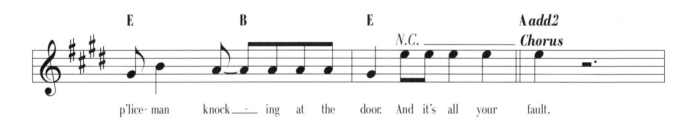

p'lice-man knock___ing at the door. And it's all your fault,

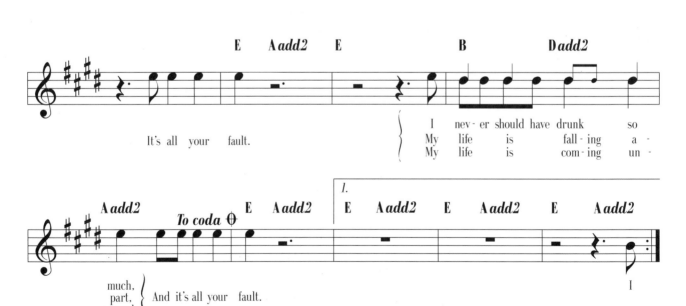

It's all your fault.

I nev-er should have drunk   so
My life is fall-ing a-
My life is com-ing un-

much,
part,   } And it's all your fault.
wound,

I

Can't think of one thing I____ can or - gan - ise,

I've lost my con - fid - ence____ and ent - er - prise.

fault, I'm gon - na quit this town,____ And it's all your

fault, I might nev - er be found,____ And it's all your fault.

2.
I parked my car in a six-foot ditch,
Might be looking at a six-month stretch,
The man says I've got two bald tyres,
And my road tax ran out last week.

3.
Down in Hooke Forest they're chopping away,
The ozone layer's getting thinner each day,
I wrecked my car and lost my job,
And Bridport's gone to the dogs.

Hampshire hog and mother, 1954

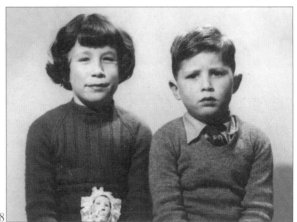

With sister Christine, Portsmouth, 1958

Gawain at Sidmouth Folk Club, 1971
Left to right: myself, Paul Downes and 'Bat' Evans

Armadas

Words and music by Steve Knightley
From 'Beat About The Bush'

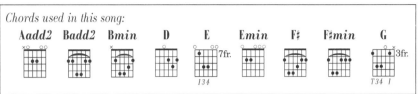

When the Ar - ma - da set sail, I fol-low'd____ the
is - lands that lay to our west. Our____ fleet was

Duke de Me - di____ - na, First bro - ken by storms and by gales,_____
beat-en and____ scat - tered, No har - bour, no hav - en, no rest,____

Then drown - ing or pray - ing a - lone;_____ Round
So few made the long jour - ney home;_____

Thous-ands were lost in sight of those shores,_____ I'll

fol - low no more.

2.
To the Malvinas we sailed,
I fought with General Menendez,
But weakened by hunger we failed,
Watching and waiting alone;
On islands that lay to our east,
An army forsaken and shattered,
Longing for shelter and peace,
So many never came home;
Brothers, fathers and sons,
We left on those shores,
I'll fight no more.

4.
The Armada still waits in the night,
For a tide to take us to war,
On islands hidden from light,
Wait Medina, Menendez and Moore;
But let them raise flags on those shores,
And stand there alone,
We're going home.

3.
To the Falklands we sailed,
I served under General Moore,
We rode out the storms and the gales,
Sleeping and dreaming alone;
For the islands lay far to our south,
But we didn't care when it mattered,
One day the truth will come out,
One day the troops will come home;
There's men seeking wealth in the seas,
All round those shores,
I'll serve them no more.

Beat About The Bush

Words and music by Steve Knightley
From 'Beat About The Bush'

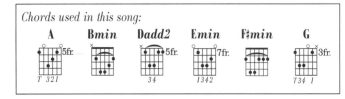

Allegro ♩ = 126
Intro

Ja - mie's head - ing for the big time, He's gon - na move to town,

Make a few con - nec - tions, Get his

face a - round; He said, "For - get a - bout the

back woods, All that driv - ing through the night,

I've been head - ing down the wrong road, Now I'll do it right,"

He says,_____ "My shoul _ - der's to the door,

All I got _ ta do is_ push,_____ I don't have time a - ny

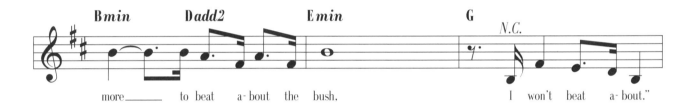

more_____ to beat a-bout the bush,   I won't beat a-bout."

2.
He waited in the doorways, he rang the right bells,
Not flying, falling, but he couldn't tell;
Soon he joined a corporation, he begs, borrows, lends,
Back driving round the country, selling to his friends.
Chorus
Instrumental
3.
Some hotel in the Midlands, we met in a bar,
Talked a bit about business, talked a bit about cars;
He started getting restless, kept looking at the clock,
Said, "How long you gonna give this? One day you got to stop."
4.
But it's five years before your fingers do what you want 'em to,
Four more to get the right voice, three to sing in tune;
Two years of questions, is there one thing you really want to say?
Half a life's preparation, half a life to make it pay.
Final choruses:
Now, got my shoulders to the door, all I gotta do is push,
I don't worry any more, I beat about the bush.

The Blind Fiddler

Traditional, arranged Knightley & Beer
From 'Show of Hands Live'

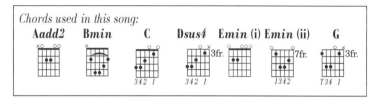

Chords used in this song:

Aadd2   Bmin   C   Dsus4   Emin (i)   Emin (ii)   G

I lost my eyes in a black-smith's shop_____ in the year of for-

ty-six._____ I was work-ing on__ a re-vol-ver_____

____ and it was out__ of__ fix; I am so sad and lone-ly__ and

I'm con-demn'd to__ roam, 'Cos I am a blind fid-dl-er and I'm a

great long way _ from_____ home._____

2.
Well, I've been down to Knoxville and I've talked to Doctor Lane.
He operated on one of my eyes, but nothing could he gain;
I am so sad and lonely and I'm condemned to roam,
'Cos I am a blind fiddler and I'm a great long way from home.

3.
Well, I've got a wife and three little kids and they all depend on me.
They're sharing all my sorrows, wherever they may be;
And I hope that they'll be careful as through this life they roam,
'Cos I am a blind fiddler and I can not help them.

Repeat verse 1

The Blue Cockade

Traditional, arranged Knightley & Beer
From 'Beat About The Bush'

Gawain (with Paul Downes and Bat Evans) supporting *Groundhogs*, Sidmouth 1971

Unknown cat, John Bickford, Paul Downes and I, Devon 1974

Exmouth School common room, playing my uncle's 12-string mandolin, 1975

Bonnie Light Horseman

Traditional, arranged Knightley & Beer
From 'Show of Hands Live'

Chords used in this song:

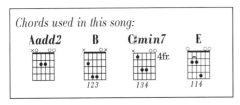

When___ Bon - ey com - man - ded his arm - ies___ to stand, And he lev - ell'd his___

can - non right___ ov - er the land, He lev - ell'd his can - non a

vic - tr'y to pur - sue, And he slew my___ light___ horse - man com - ing home from the

war. Bro - ken - heart - ed I'll___ wan - der, Bro - ken - heart - ed___ I'll re -

main, Since my bon - nie___ light___ horse - man in the wars he was slain.

2.
If I was a small bird and had wings for to fly,
I would fly o'er the salt sea where my true love does lie,
And with my fond wings I would beat o'er the sea,
And I'd kiss the cold lips that lie cold in the clay,
Broken-hearted I'll wander, broken-hearted I'll remain,
Since my bonnie light horseman in the wars he was slain.

3.
The dove she laments for her darling as she flies,
Oh where, tell me where, is my true love? she cries,
And where in this world is there one to compare,
With my bonnie light horseman who was slain in the war?
Broken-hearted I'll wander, broken-hearted I'll remain,
Since my bonnie light horseman in the wars he was slain.

Captains

Words and music by Steve Knightley
From 'Lie Of The Land'

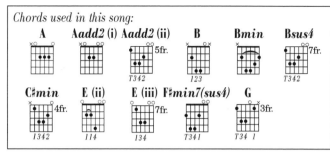

Moderato ♩ = 108

High a-bove___ the earth,___

___ hours be-fore___ we land,___ Morn - ing slow___ - ly breaks___

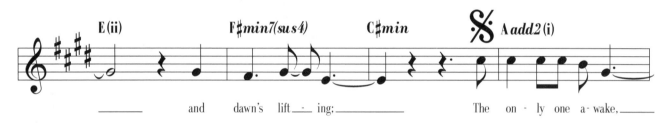

___ and dawn's lift___ - ing;___ The on - ly one a-wake,___

___ so gent - ly in___ my hands,___ I trace a hun___ - dred lives___

___ through dark___ - ness drift___ - ing.___ I will bring you back,___

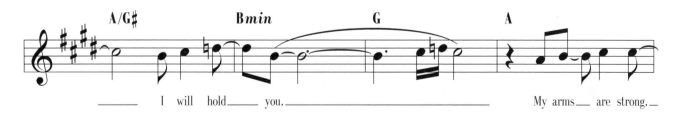

___ I will hold___ you,___ My arms___ are strong,___

they will en - fold you.

For we search on ev-'ry side, for a

com-pass and a guide, Some-one with the at - las and the

chart, Oh we say, "Please be the cap — tain of my

heart, my heart."

We turn

2.
Far out at sea, a hundred miles from shore,
A storm begins to rise and the tide's turning;
Driving wind and rain to try my skill once more,
Testing yet again all my craft and learning;
Oh, my love, to calmer seas I will steer you,
And you'll be safe while I am near you.

3.
We turn away from town and steer towards the west,
The rain beats on the road as the sun is setting;
You close your eyes and soon you're sleeping,
And as you dream you're in my keeping;
At last when you awake and look around you,
I've brought you back and I have found you.

Cars

Words and music by Steve Knightley
From 'Beat About The Bush'

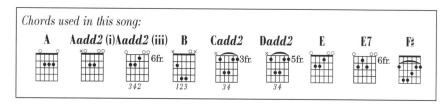

Wel-come to Bri-tain.

I got up at dawn___ to drive to the coast,___

It's fif-ty miles,___ two hours at the most,___ I'm feel-ing good, the

weath-er is fine,___ Drive down___ my___ road, guess what I find?___

Cars!___ As far as the eye can see, just___ cars!___

I would have been there hours___ a-go, But there's miles___ and miles and miles of___ cars!___

2.
I take a chance, take the next right,
Drive down the back streets, nothing in sight,
Picking up speed, making good time,
Take the next left, guess what I find?

3.
(Some hours later)
You know, I got room for five but I sit here alone,
I'm giving up, I'm going home,
I drive up and down outside my place,
I want to park but I can't find a space for...

Lanchester Poly, Coventry 1976

Busking with Paul Downes and Phil Beer
at the Isle of Man Festival, 1976

Bob O'Connor

The first ever press shot with
Warwick Downes, Brighton 1977

Caught In The Rain

Words and music by Steve Knightley and Matt Clifford
From 'Show of Hands Live'

2.
Now that you've gone I think about you all the time,
I haunt the rooms where we lay when we were young and when you were mine.
'Cos I let you free, I just opened the door,
Into the sky I watched you soar,
I loved you, I cried, darling, I called out your name,
You said, "How could our love survive now that it's tame?"

Class Of Seventy-Three

Words and music by Steve Knightley
From 'Beat About The Bush'

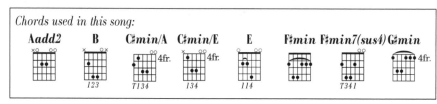

Mi - chael's a long dis - tance dri - ver;

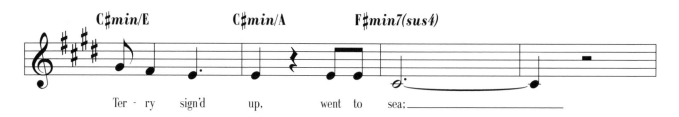

Ter - ry sign'd up, went to sea;

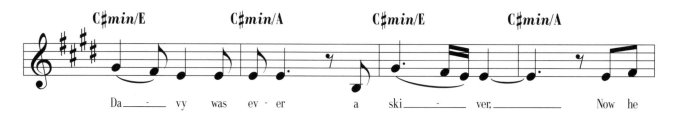

Da - vy was ev - er a ski - ver; Now he

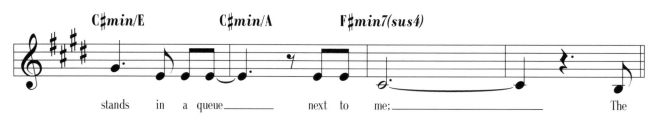

stands in a queue next to me; The

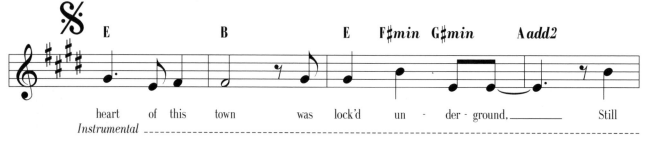

heart of this town was lock'd un - der - ground, Still

Instrumental --------

E   B   A *add2*

beat - ing,   there   is   no   key.   Now the

E   B   E   F♯*min*   G♯*min*   A *add2*

boys   have   all___   gone,   But   when   we   were   young, ___   In   the

E   B   A *add2*

class   of ___   sev - en - ty - three, ___   A

E   B   C♯*min*/E   C♯*min*/A

min - er   was   some- thing/one   to   be. ___

C♯*min*/E   C♯*min*/A   C♯*min*/E   C♯*min*/A   C♯*min*/E   C♯*min*/A   C♯*min*/E

Fine

Dal Segno 𝄋

Taken whilst playing with *The Steve Knightley Band* in
Cheltenham, 1976. Other members of the band included
Dick Cadbury on guitar and Neil Waterman on bass

Columbus (Didn't Find America)

Words and music by Steve Knightley
From Columbus (Didn't Find America)

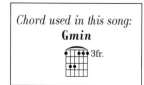
Allegro ♩ = 126

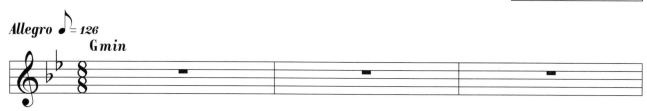

Co - lum - bus did - n't find A - me - ri - ca,_____

It was - n't lost, it was al - ways there,_____ I

won't cel - e - brate five hun - dred years,_____

Plund - er - ing wealth and scat - ter - ing tears._____

The San - ta Ma - ri - a sail'd out of the sun,____

War - ri - or priests, cros - ses and guns;____ On a

thous - and tides in a mil - li - on ways,____ Came

ca - rry - ing sick - ness, cat - tle and slaves.____ Co -

2.
Alvarado and the Cortez,
Almagro, Pizzaro and all the rest,
They raped the land and stole the sun,
Thieves, butchers, every one.

3.
The forest stretched from shore to shore,
Water was clean and the air was pure,
Now driven from the land, living in slums,
Without names, without tongues.

4.
In fourteen hundred and ninety-two,
Columbus sailed the ocean blue,
Now the new world sickens and the old grows fat,
Might have been much better if the earth was flat.

Day Has Come

Words and music by Steve Knightley
From 'Beat About The Bush'

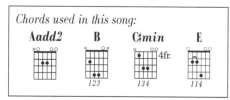

Chords used in this song:

Aadd2   **B**   **C#min**   **E**

Moderato ♩ = 112

Intro

Day___ has___ come,___   I pull the cur-___ tains and shake___
___ come,___   The dawn has brought___ a sil-___
___ come,___   Still my twi-___ light___ friend___
Instrumental ....
___ come,___   The morn-ing calls___ me___ on___

___ my head,___ A dream re-mains___ though the dark___ has fled, It
___ ent guest,___ Who woke in sleep___ and now___ won't rest, A
___ is near,___ She gent-ly whis-___ pers in___ my ear.
___ my way,___ I'm walk-ing through the ear-___ ly grey, The

weaves the room like spi___ der thread,
mid - night friend the night___ has left, Not
Words that on - ly I___ can hear. She

steps be - side me fade___ a - way, I

E (Aadd2)   **Last time to coda** ⊕

Spa - ces talk___ and sha - dows smile, They
close e - nough___ to hold or touch, I
stands just where___ the mir - ror ends, I'm

nev - er want___ to sleep a - gain, If

Don't It Feel Good
Words and music by Steve Knightley
From 'Show of Hands Live'

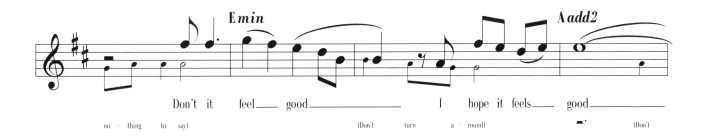

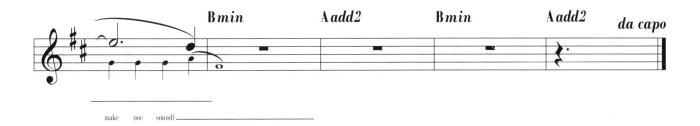

Don't it feel___ good_____ I hope it feels___ good_____

no · thing to say) (Don't turn a · round) (Don't

make one sound)_____

2.
I've known for a while,
That it's gone wrong,
When we don't smile,
How can we hang on?
So gather your thoughts,
All the words you throw,
Leave nothing but tears,
So leave me alone.
Chorus

3.
The damage is done,
Our moment is past,
We've wasted our time,
It could never last;
As you turn to go,
I whisper your name,
Now that I know,
I won't see you again.
Chorus

Posing by Brighton Pier, 1978

Exile

Words and music by Steve Knightley
From 'Show of Hands Live'

Section — When it thun-ders from the emp-ty skies_____ I shall_____ be there._____

_____ No- one to hold_____ you when the storm___ birds fly,_____ Is

D.C. al coda — there no-one left_____ to___ care?

Coda — Here's a gen-er-ra_____tion

wait - ing still,_____ We've got year_____ aft - er

year to kill:_____ But no go-ing home._____ No go-ing_____

a tempo — home. There's_____ no_____ go___ing home.

2.
I can dream before the break of day,
That I'm back with you again,
Then the morning blows it all away,
Leaves an echo of your name;
Still a thousand miles lie between us,
Where we're waking up alone,
What if I could cross a hundred borders?
But there's no going home, there's no going home.

3.
I'm searching rumours with my hollow plans,
When all I want is what's mine,
Lost and lonely in a foreign land,
I'm left too far behind the lines.
I want to tear down the walls between us,
But I can't do it all alone,
A million spaces in the earth to fill,
To coda

Friends

Words and music by Steve Knightley
From 'Backlog 1987-1991'

Moderato ♩ = 116

Intro.

Well, I'm glad I found___ you here, I hope you're do-ing
what you like;___ And though it's been___ a year,___
We're gon-na sit up half___ the night;___ I hope be-neath the sur-
___ face we're___ the same,___ And though the mus-___ ic's chang'd,___
___ the song___ re-mains.___ Cir-cum-

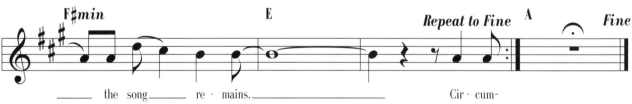

2.
Circumstances broke the spell,
Sent us all our separate ways,
But it wasn't so hard to tell,
We just began another phase;
So many stages I recall
And when they seemed final,
We rode them all.

3.
Now there's time to look around,
Let old memories fill the room,
And just on the edge of sound,
Someone's playing out of tune;
What does it matter how long it lasts,
With the old familiar faces
To help time pass?

4.
And when the coming days have long
Pulled us out of sight,
And pressure begins to weigh,
Don't let it in without a fight;
"Time is money," is all they say,
Believe that and you've
Thrown your friends away.

Repeat verse 1 to finish

The Galway Farmer

Words and music by Steve Knightley
From 'Beat About The Bush'

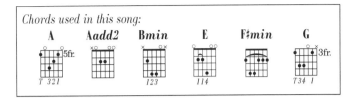

Chords used in this song:
A   Aadd2   Bmin   E   F#min   G

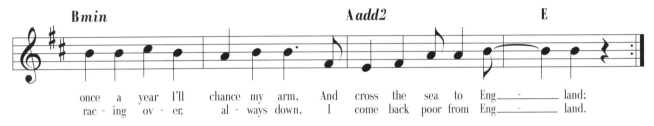

Fast ♩ = 100

Bmin ... **Aadd2**

(Verse 1 freely)

I   work my days on a   Gal - way farm, In the   sun and rain,___ wind   and storm,__ But
I'll   scrimp and save   two   thous- and pounds,   Spend the week in Chelt - 'nham town.__ But the

Bmin   **Aadd2**   **E**

once   a   year I'll   chance my arm,   And   cross the sea to   Eng_____ land;
rac - ing ov - er,   al - ways down,   I   come back poor from Eng_____ land.

(A tempo)   **Bmin**   **G**

I   dream'd one night be - fore___ I   left,___ A   coal - black mare with a   white star chest,
I   rose at dawn and drove___ all   day,___ Think- ing, wond'r- ing___ all   the way.

A   **F#min**   **E**

Cross'd the line__ and___ beat the rest,___ I   came back rich to   Gal_____ - way;
Lad - y Luck__ have you come to stay,___ Or   steal a - way my morn_____ - ing?

3.
When I got to Cheltenham town, Irish faces all around,
No bed or mattress to be found, I slept on the hillside;
Spent three days in the viewing ring, saw the horses they led in,
Just when I was giving in I stood and stared in wonder.

4.
With stamping hooves and steaming breath, a coal-black mare with a
white star chest,
I ran my finger down the list, matched the name and the number;
Lady Luck had come half-way, the horse's name was 'Galway Bay',
Twenty-to-one the odds that day, I went to make my wager.

5.
I counted out two thousand pounds, held it high, slapped it down,
The bookie smiled but made no sound, I knew what he was thinking;
The biggest loser in the land, a pounding heart, shaking hand,
I made my way up to the stand, the horses came to order.

6.
But at the first, she nearly fell, I cursed my farmer's luck to hell,
The second and third took quite well, way behind the leaders;
Then moving sweetly from the back she found the rails and caught the
pack,
Ten to go and from the track the hooves were drumming thunder.

7.
She's catching horses one by one, bridle flashing in the sun,
Eight to go, a mile to run, two were up before her;
On the straight, down they sped, left one at the last for dead,
Caught the next and by a head she came home the winner.

8.
So I came back to my Galway farm a wiser and a richer man,
Never again I'll chance my arm or cross the sea to England;
'Cos Lady Luck was mine that day, I held her close, I went my way,
Now I raise my glass to Galway Bay and the dream of a Galway farmer.

The Hook Of Love

Words and music by Steve Knightley
From 'Beat About The Bush'

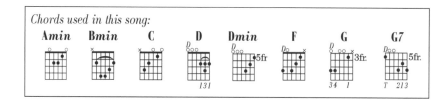

Chords used in this song:
Amin Bmin C D Dmin F G G7

Andante ♩ = 80

D   Amin G   D   Bmin   D   Amin G   D   Bmin

(Fine)

She turns_____ o - ver_____ deep in the night,__

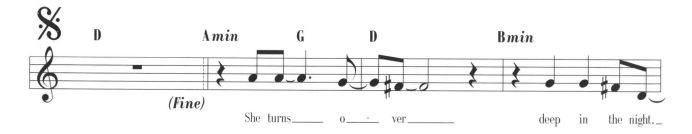

_____ Lis - tens to him sleep____ - ing, rea - ches for___ the light,__

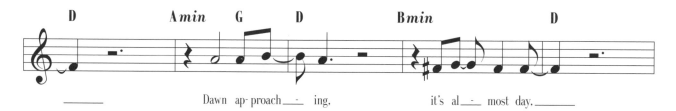

_____ Dawn ap - proach___ - ing, it's al___ - most day,_____

She could___ be wak___ - ing a thou - sand miles___ a - way;_____

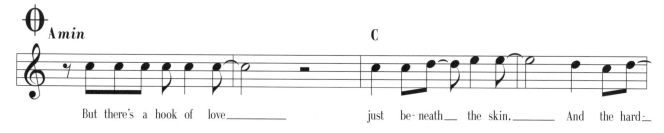

But there's a hook of love_____ just be - neath___ the skin,_____ And the hard___

___ er that___ she pulls___ a - way, The deep - er it___ goes in, ___

___ There's an is - land out___ there some___ - where,

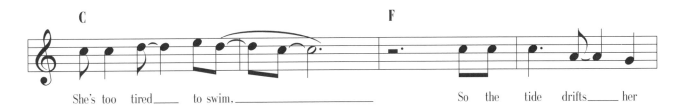

She's too tired___ to swim,___ So the tide drifts___ her

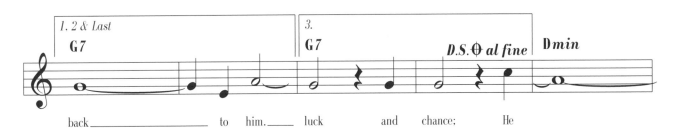

back___ to him.___ luck and chance; He

2.
She hates the cold, he hates the heat,
She loves the country, he needs the street,
He quick to borrow, she's swift to lend,
He's always breaking and she wants to mend;
But on a hook of love they turn and they twist,
Wounding one another with every lie and every kiss,
Like gypsies with daggers, they're tied at the wrist,
And they're getting much too close to miss.

3.
In all the stories when she was young,
They were perfect partners for everyone,
You had to keep searching to find the other half,
Staring out the window she wants to laugh;
We stumble through the darkness stretching out our hands,
Just hoping that we'll find someone else to understand,
That we're looking out for shelter, longing for romance,
But leaving it to luck and chance.

4.
He sits down at the table and they share a look,
It only lasts a second, but she could write a book,
For a thousand things were said in the moment that it took,
To tie another line on the hook.

The Hunter

Words and music by Steve Knightley
From 'Lie Of The Land'

land, It's al-ways___ been this way,___ you don't un-der-stand, There's pow'r in___ my

hands when I hold on___-to the reins, 'Cos the hunt's in___ my blood, the

chase is___ in my veins"_____ "Come and join_____ us"

1.

"Come on!"

2. & 3.

"Come and join_____ us" I said

"No!" I___ said "No!" to the hun-ter.___

D.S. al fine 𝄋 F

I___ said

2.

I walked home, I knew that we'd met before,
He was looking for votes, he came right and knocked on my door,
We talked for a while, he turned and he lifted his voice,
"Remember these words next time you're making your choice:
"You have the right to win, they have the right to lose:
"The right to spend your money anyway you choose,
"There's power in your hands when you hold onto the reins,
"'Cos the hunt's in your blood, the chase is in your veins."

3.

I dreamt last night I rode with the hounds on the hill,
The fields and the farms flew by, we moved in for the kill,
And the pack was howling, this is the law of the land,
It's the law of the jungle, the market, the nature of man;
Then we rode into the sea, were swept out on the tide,
I woke in a sweat, threw my window open wide,
Horseman in the distance was riding in the rain,
Stretching out his hands, calling out my name.

I'll Put A Stake Through His Heart

Words and music by Steve Knightley
From 'Show of Hands Live'

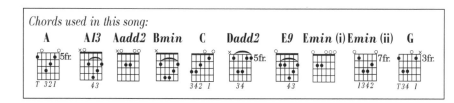

Andante ♩ = *88*

Intro.

Verse

I read___ your let - ters___ when you're not___ a - round, I___

fol - low___ your car as___ you drive through___ the town; I call you___ at

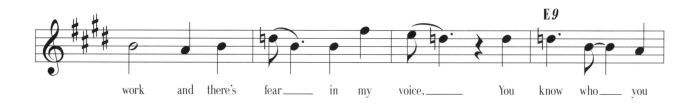

work and there's fear___ in my voice,___ You know who___ you

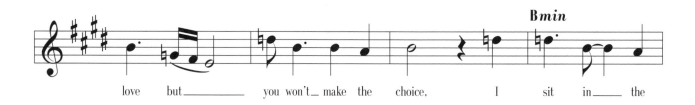

love but_____ you won't___ make the choice. I sit in___ the

si - lence___ and stare at___ the dark_____ I'll put___ a

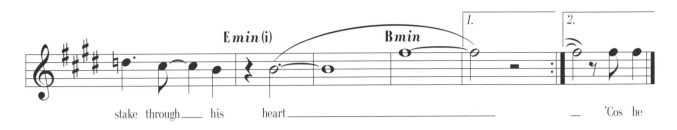

stake through ___ his heart _____ ___ 'Cos he

Section

stands in ___ the street ___ and the dogs start ___ to ___ bark, You

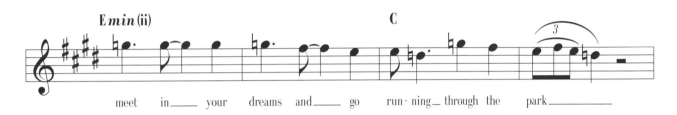

meet in ___ your dreams and ___ go run-ning ___ through the park _____

Hides from ___ the day ___ -light, creeps aft ___ -ter dark; I'll put ___ a

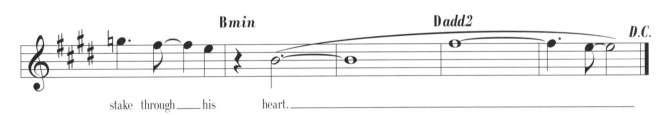

stake through ___ his heart. _____

2.
Somebody rings and you run to the 'phone,
I think he calls back when I'm not at home,
You visit friends, you get back so late,
I ask where you've been and you hesitate;
I hold us together, he pulls us apart,
I'll put a stake through his heart.

3.
You talk in your sleep and I start to pray,
You're wearing a cross, will it keep him away?
'Cos his teeth sharp like needles, you don't feel the bite,
I've stood back too long, now I will fight;
'Cos I know where he hides and I'll make my mark,
I'll put a stake through his heart.
Repeat last two lines

I Still Wait

Words and music by Steve Knightley
From 'Show of Hands Live'

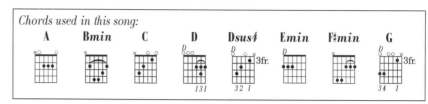

Chords used in this song:
A Bmin C D Dsus4 Emin F♯min G

Allegro ♩ = 144

Intro

You were writ-ing your let-ters,_____ As I read your name_

_____ in the sand, I walk'd to the edge of the wa____ter,_____

Hold-ing your note in my___ hand; You're tell-ing me that it's

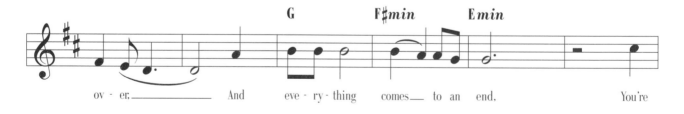

ov-er,_____ And eve-ry-thing comes___ to an end, You're

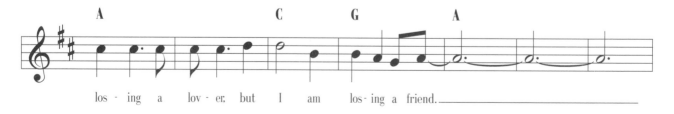

los-ing a lov-er, but I am los-ing a friend._____

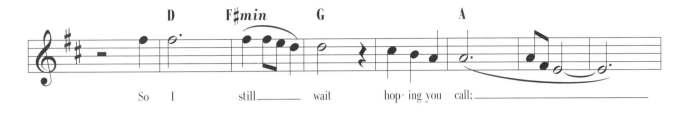

So I still_____ wait hop-ing you call;_____

Bet-ter____ a lit-tle___ love late than no love at all._____

_____ I I'm_____ hear-ing your voice and I call out your name,

Turn back the pag-es, hur-ry home to me a-gain._____

I still_____ wait. I still_____ wait.

2.
I stand at the edge of the mirror,
Where the daylight begins,
Hearing your breath like a whisper,
Waiting for darkness to end;
I really thought I had grown strong,
And this couldn't happen again,
But you've proved me wrong,
You showed me I hadn't changed.

3.
You put ice in the heart of my season,
You took light from the soul of my day,
You gave me no reason,
You just turn away.

The Keeper

Words and music by Steve Knightley
From 'Lie Of The Land'

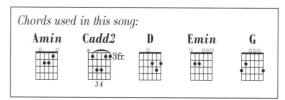

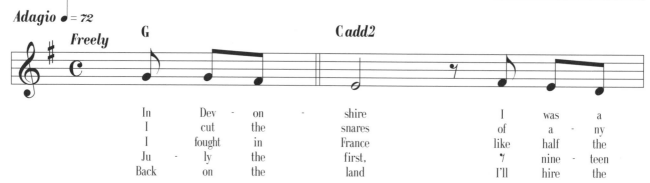

In Dev - on - shire I was a
I cut the snares of a ny
I fought in France like half the
Ju - ly the first, nine - teen
Back on the land I'll hire the

keep - er, Half my life I liv'd out -
poa - cher, Ris - ing hours be - fore the
coun - ty, With all the skill I learnt at
six - teen, We ear - ly rose, pass'd round the
beat - ers, And when the 'glor - ious twelfth' has

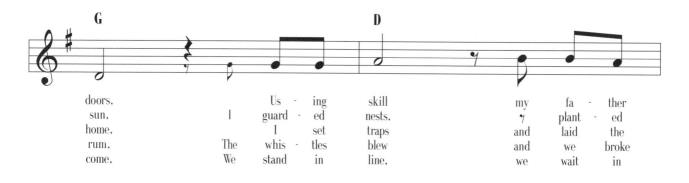

doors, Us - ing skill my fa - ther
sun, I guard - ed nests, plant - ed
home, I set traps and laid the
rum, The whis - tles blew and we broke
come, We stand in line, we wait in

taught me, On land that edg'd the o - pen
cov - ers, Then drove the birds to - wards the
wire, The earth grew red as Dev - on's
cov - er, And walk'd in line to - wards the
sil - ence, And walk once more to - wards the

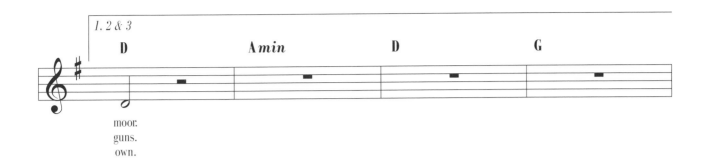

1, 2 & 3

D   A min   D   G

moor.
guns.
own.

4 & 5

D   A min

guns,   We   walk'd   to - wards   the   wait - ing
guns,   We   walk   to - wards   the   wait - ing

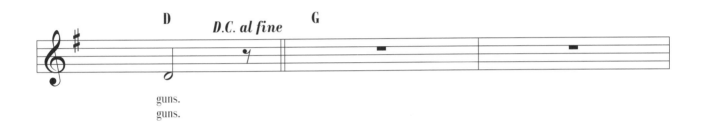

D   *D.C. al fine*   G

guns.
guns.

Jack - ie   boy,   Sing   thee   well,   Hey   down,   A -

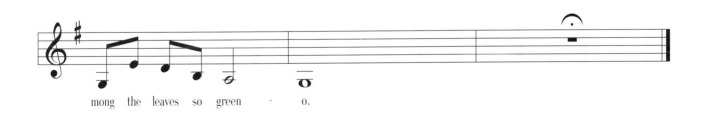

mong   the   leaves   so   green   -   o.

The Last Picture Show

Words and music by Steve Knightley
From 'Backlog 1987-1991'

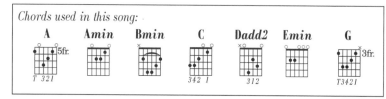

Chords used in this song:

A   Amin   Bmin   C   Dadd2   Emin   G

Noth-ing chan-ges in this town but street___ lights,_____ Night-life flick-ers

falls_____ by mid-___night,_____ A con-crete cage I'm trapp'd in-side,

two floors high an' a half-a-mile wide,_____ Mov-ing in the dark___ and I'm

leav-ing be-hind___ and I take flight,_____ I real-ly take flight.___

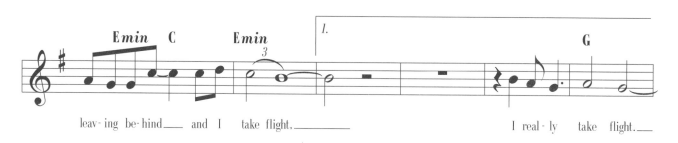

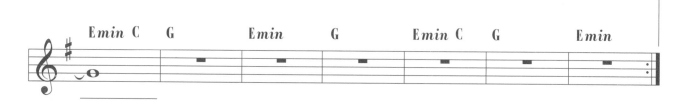

_____

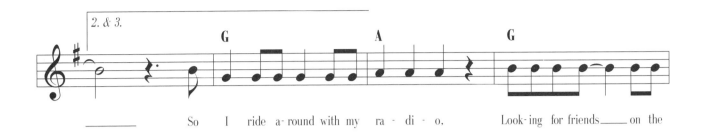

So I ride a-round with my ra-di-o, Look-ing for friends on the

late night show, Mu-sic takes me, I let go, Ride a-round with my

ra-di-o, When I ride a-round with my ra-di-o, wo

wo, There's just one last pic-ture show. As a

shad-ow walks ov-er main street,

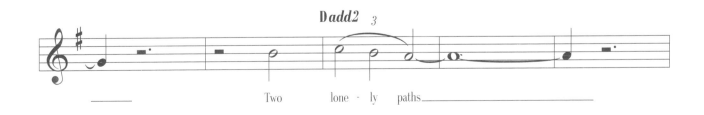

Two lone-ly paths

that will soon meet,_____ From sep'-rate ways_____

_____ through the long night,_____ I

see your face_____ in my head - lights,_____

A tempo D.C. al coda

_____ In my head - lights._____

Coda

Ad lib to fade

2.
People look away when I talk of leaving,
In their eyes, it's only me I'm deceiving,
Look at my best friend, younger than me,
A car and a job and he thinks he's free,
But he better watch out now he talks like a has-been.
3.
I'm gonna move to the city, find me a job in the mainstream,
I'm treading water, living life in a daydream,
As long as I'm stuck in a one-street town,
Let me travel on a rock'n'roll sound,
And long for the day something else to believe in.

Low Down In The Broome

Traditional, arranged Knightley & Beer
From 'Show of Hands Live'

Chords used in this song:

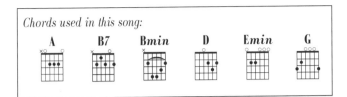

'Twas on last Mon-day's morn-ing the day a-point—ed was, To

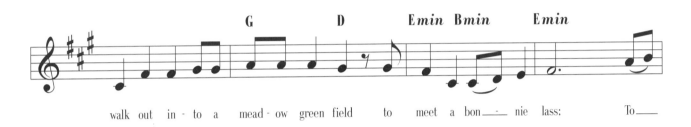

walk out in-to a mead-ow green field to meet a bon—nie lass; To—

meet a bon—nie—las—sie, to bear her com-pa-ny,——— For she's

low down, she's in the broome, A-wait-ing there—for—me.

2.
I looked over my left shoulder to see who I could see,
And there I spied my own true love come tripping down to me;
Her heart being brisk and bonnie to bear my company,
For she's low down, she's in the broome,
A-waiting there for me.

3.
I took hold of her lily-white hand and happy I sang my heart,
And now we are together I hope we ne'er shall part;
Part, my dear, oh never, until the day I die,
For she's low down, she's in the broome,
A-waiting there for me.

Lovers, Never Friends

Words and music by Steve Knightley
From 'Backlog 1987-1991'

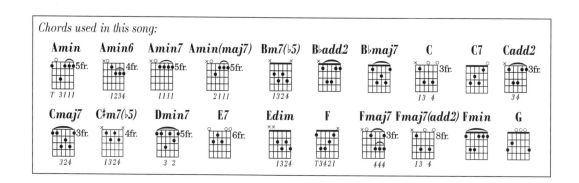

Andante ♩ = 84

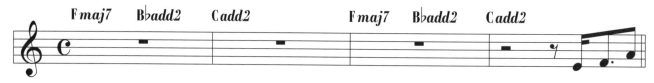

F maj7   B♭add2   C add2   F maj7   B♭add2   C add2

You heard my

F maj7(add2) D min7   C   F maj7(add2) D min7   C

voice   and turn'd a - round,   Catch-ing   laugh-ter___ in the___crowd,_____   If we___

F maj7(add2) D min7   C   Bm7(♭5)   A min   F   G   E7

lose   the love we've___ found.   Our smiles___ will fade,   we'll laugh too   loud,   We'll be

Refrain

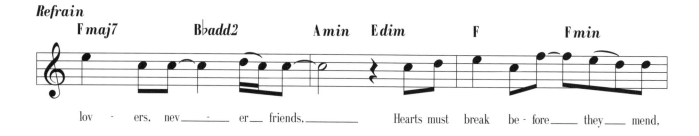

F maj7   B♭add2   A min   E dim   F   F min

lov - ers,   nev_____ - er___ friends,_____   Hearts must   break   be - fore_____ they___ mend,

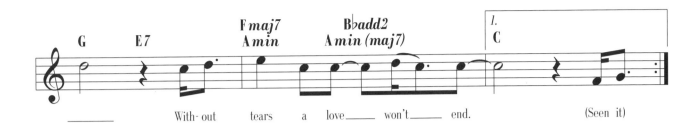

With-out tears a love____ won't____ end. (Seen it)

We'll be lov-ers ne--ver friends.____

You want to change____ the sit-u-a-tion,____

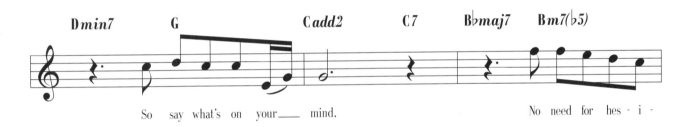

So say what's on your____ mind. No need for hes-i-

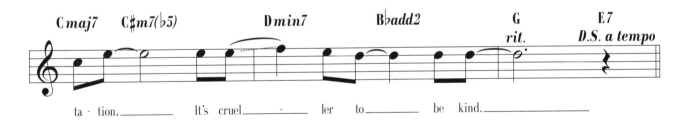

ta-tion,____ It's cruel____-ler to____ be kind.____

2.
Seen it time and time again,
The flame grows cold, it all goes wrong,
The one who tries to spare the pain,
Will keep the other hanging on.

3.
We think that we can have it all,
With the strength to make it right,
We think the rain will never fall,
We'll stop the day from turning night.

The Man In Green

Words and music by Steve Knightley
From 'Lie Of The Land'

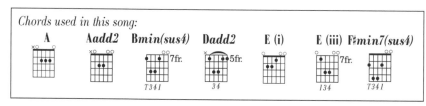

Chords used in this song:

A   Aadd2   Bmin(sus4)   Dadd2   E (i)   E (iii)   F#min7(sus4)

Andante ♩ = 84

Intro

F#min7(sus4)

Verse

F#min7(sus4)   Aadd2   E (iii)

Storm - clouds   in   the   dis_____tance,   The   sky   speaks   of

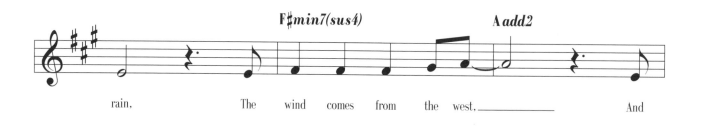

F#min7(sus4)   Aadd2

rain,   The   wind   comes   from   the   west,_____   And

E (iii)   Bmin(sus4)

aut - umn's   here   a - gain,_____   As   the   dark - ness

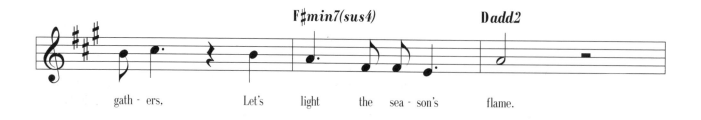

F#min7(sus4)   Dadd2

gath - ers,   Let's   light   the   sea - son's   flame.

Chorus   **A**   **E(i)**

With fire and wat - er, land and sea,_____ The

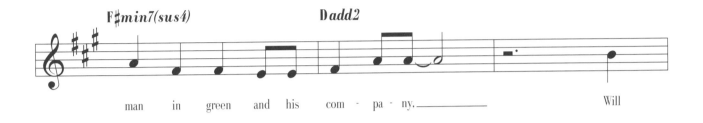

F♯min7(sus4)   **Dadd2**

man in green and his com - pa - ny,_____ Will

A   **E(i)**   **F♯min7(sus4)**

take the land_____ and shake the throne,_____ Make his stand_____ and

Dadd2

claim his own._____

2.
The countryside is restless,
The harvest almost home,
Someone stirs the woodland,
And walks the paths alone,
Marching men approaching,
And hunting horns are blown:
Chorus

3.
Days we will remember,
A time we won't forget,
Hours of celebration,
Long after sun has set,
Voices joined together,
Will raise the country yet:
Chorus
Repeat first verse and chorus

Brighton, 1977

Rob O'Connor

Man of War

Words and music by Steve Knightley
From 'Show of Hands Live'

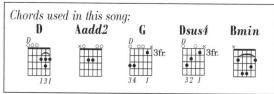

Chords used in this song:

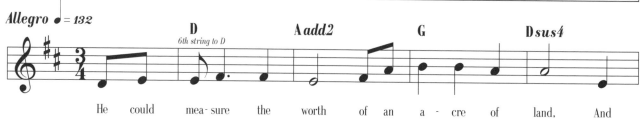

He could mea- sure the worth of an a - cre of land, And

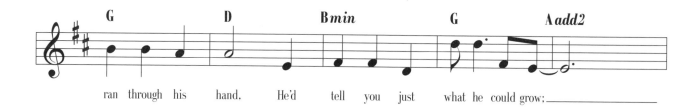

say when the wind would blow; Reach down to the earth as it

ran through his hand, He'd tell you just what he could grow;_____

His fam - 'ly had stood on these rid - ges and hills,

Sev - en gen - er - ra - tions or more, Born to the fields, the

streams and the sky,_____ Now he's a man_____ of war._____ Strong___

_____ winds,_____ bring him back,_____ Haul a - way_____

Coda

When he sleeps, then he dreams he's a far - mer a -

gain_____ but he wakes as a man of war.

2.
When his father fell, the land was carved,
One piece for every son;
There was barely enough for a family to feed,
Hardly enough for one;
So he went to the harbour, stood on the quay,
Saw the waves crash to the shore,
Turning the cries of a man of the land,
Into a man of war.
Strong winds, bring him back, haul away.

3.
Now the ocean's cold, the tide running deep,
He dreams he is home at last;
Running handfuls of grain through his fingers like sand,
Before on the water it's cast;
But it falls on the deep, goes drifting down,
To the dark of the ocean's floor;
When he sleeps, he dreams, he's a landsman again,
But he wakes as a man of war.
Strong winds, bring him back, haul away.
To coda

Rob O'Connor

Brighton bus shelter, 1978

Caught at *The Cheats*' first gig
at the Buccaneer, Brighton 1979

The Cheats, including John
Hoare, Neil Waterman and
Les Maas, Brighton, 1979

Nine Hundred Miles

Traditional, arranged Knightley & Beer
From 'Beat About The Bush'

Chords used in this song:

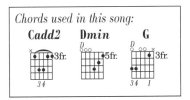

Moderato ♩= 128 **Dmin**
6th string to D

Walk - ing down the track, Tears in my eyes, Try-ing to read a

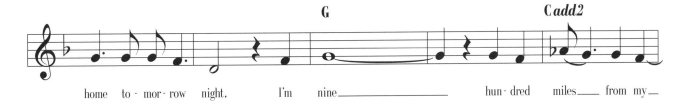

let - ter from my home; If this train runs me right, I'll be

home to - mor - row night, I'm nine_____ hun - dred miles___ from my___

_____ home._____ I'll

2.
I'll pawn you my watch,
Pawn you my chain,
Pawn you my gold and diamond rings;
If this train runs me right,
I'll be home tomorrow night,
I'm nine hundred miles from my home.

3.
If my woman tells me so,
I will railroad no more,
Hang around this shack all day long;
If this train runs me right,
I'll be home tomorrow night,
I'm nine hundred miles from my home.

4.
This train I ride on,
Is a hundred coaches long,
Hear the whistle blow a million miles;
If this train runs me right,
I'll be home tomorrow night,
Nine hundred miles from my home.

5.
I'm walking down the track,
I got tears in my eyes,
Trying to read a letter from my home;
If this train runs me right,
I'll be home tomorrow night,
I'm nine hundred miles from my home,
Nine hundred miles from my home,
I'm nine hundred miles from my home,
Nine hundred miles.

The Oak

Words and music by Steve Knightley
From 'Beat About The Bush'

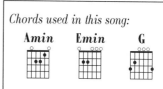

Chords used in this song:
Amin   Emin   G

Moderato ♩. = 108

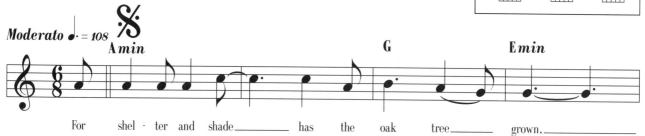

For shel - ter and shade_____ has the oak tree_____ grown,_____

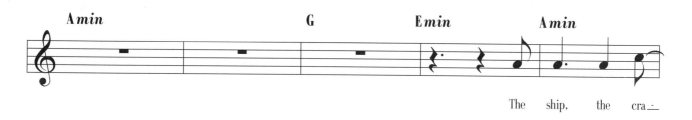

The ship, the cra -

_____ dle,_____ the hearth and_____ home;_____

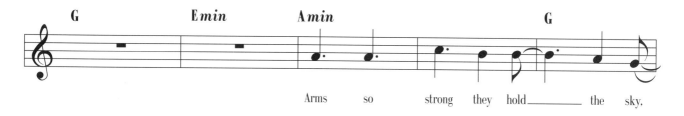

Arms so strong they hold_____ the sky,

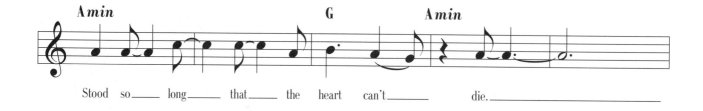

Stood so_____ long_____ that_____ the heart can't_____ die._____

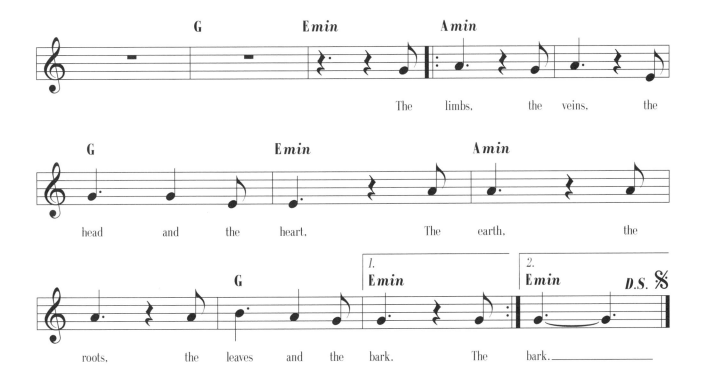

The limbs, the veins, the

head and the heart, The earth, the

roots, the leaves and the bark. The bark.

2.
Tear the branch and your crops will fail,
Break the bough and your fleet won't sail;
It cries when the black rain burns,
Trees die when the seas return.

3.
A dozen generations the oak tree's grown,
(The limbs, the veins, the head and the heart)
The roots reach deep to the rocks and bones.
(The earth, the roots, the leaves and the bark)

A ***Total Strangers*** press shot taken in
London, 1980, including Neil Waterman,
Gus Hayle and John Hoare

Short Stories at the Cartoon Club in Croydon, 1981, with Barry Wickens and Julian Dyke

More posing, London 1981, for a ***Cheats*** press shot

Rob O'Connor

Short Stories at the Cartoon Club (again), showing Barry and Les Maas, in 1981

Poor Wayfaring Stranger

Traditional, arranged Knightley & Beer
From 'Beat About The Bush'

2.
I know dark clouds will gather round me,
I know my way is rough and steep,
But golden trails lie out before me,
And there I'll lay my head to sleep;
I'm going back to meet my mother,
She said she'd meet me when I come,
I'm only going over Jordan, I'm only going over home.

The Preacher

Words and music by Steve Knightley
From 'Lie Of The Land'

I am the preach— - er on the is— - land,_____ sev - en

years___ liv'd a- lone,_____ I try and bring___ some com - fort

to a world_____ of sea and stone;_____

There are___ no trees on the is——- land, no- where to shelt—

—— er or hide,_____ The men tear the rocks___ from the quar—

—— ry___ or take their chanc——- es on the tide._____

I fell in love with the wife of the man who lays_____ the fuse:_____

_____ When I heard the thund-er from the earth,_____ I

knew I had to choose,_____ Be - tween_____ fall_____ ing_____

_____ and my cold,_____ cold_____ call - ing._____

Ooo_-_ooo_____

2.
They used to walk beside the water, voices blown by the wind,
And I would watch from the distance and I'd dream I was him;
Then he found work on the mainland, oh, how I prayed,
That something would tear them apart, force her to stay,
Oh, I was falling and the cold, cold was calling.

3.
Next day, they called me to the quarry, there was something badly wrong,
A man lay crushed by falling rock, his life almost gone;
I knew his face in the darkness: I didn't need to know the name,
All my prayers were answered and I was the one to blame;
I closed his eyes and looked up, she was running through the rain,
She took him in her arms and begged the Lord to give him life again,
And if I should live all the seven ages of man,
Seven tides will never wash all the blood from my hands.

4.
I am the preacher on the island: I live on my own,
I used to pray but now I leave my maker well alone;
Just like the chapels on the island my heart's dark and overgrown,
I try to find some comfort on a world of sea and stone.

Ratcliffe Highway

Traditional, arranged Knightley & Beer
From 'Lie Of The Land'

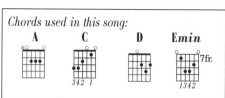

Chords used in this song:
A   C   D   Emin

Allegro ♩ = 152

Emin

As I was go-ing up Lon-don, from
dox-y came roll-ing up to me, and she

D

Wapp-ing to Rat-cliffe High-way, I
ask'd if I'd mon-ey to sport, Bring a

Emin

chanc'd to drop in-to an ale-house, to
bot-tle of wine, change a guin-ea, and

(C)   D   Emin (A)

spend a long night and a day,_____ A young
quick-ly she said, "That's the sort"._____ When the

2.
When the bottle was put on the table,
There were glasses for everyone,
When I asked for the rest of my guinea,
She tipped me the verse of a song;
The lady flew into a passion,
And she placed both her hands on her hips,
She said, "Sailor, you don't know our fashion,
"Do you think you're on board of your ship?"

3.
"Well, if it's your fashion to rob me,
"It's a fashion I'll never abide,
"So give me the rest of my guinea,
"Or I'll give to you a broadside."
The bottle it stood on the table,
I launched it straightway at her head,
And down she fell just like thunder,
"God save us, he's killed me," she said.

4.
Well, a gold watch it stood on the mantle,
And for the change of my guinea I seized,
And I ran down the back stairs like thunder,
Saying, "Damn my old eyes, I'm well pleased."
The night being dark in my favour,
To the river quickly I sped,
And I jumped on a ship bound for Deptford,
And back to my mess-mates I fled.

5.
So, come all you jolly young fellows,
That ramble down Ratcliffe Highway,
If you chance to drop into this alehouse,
Be careful how long you do stay;
For the wine and the women entice you,
'Til your mind it is quickly deranged,
When you ask for the rest of your guinea,
You can go to the devil for change.

Safe As Houses

Words and music by Steve Knightley
From 'Lie Of The Land'

Chords used in this song:

Aadd2   Bmin   D   Dsus4   G

Andante ♩ = 88

Bars on ev-'ry win-dow, There's a chain up-on the door, This home's no cas-tle, no shel-ter a-ny-more; What's left worth steal-ing when you live in fear? Like pris-'ners we sleep, Safe as hous-es a-round here, a-round here.

2.
No movement stirs the air,
And smoke drifts from no fire,
One thing enters freely,
The signals down the wires;
A screen lights up the darkness,
While outside footsteps pass,
We watch and we are watched,
Safe as houses behind glass, behind glass.

3.
A world of information,
Sending static into space,
In communication,
But never face to face;
Reaching out for friendship,
Means reaching for a 'phone,
We're stretching out our hands,
Safe as houses all alone, all alone.

Santiago

Words and music by Steve Knightley
From 'Show of Hands Live'

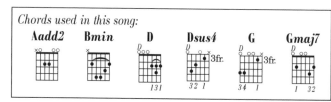

From the ports___ of the west___ we sail'd in-to the___ sun,___

South A - mer - i - ca___ bound___ a jour - ney be - gun;___

Lights go-ing on___ in the Barr___ - i - os half___ the world a -

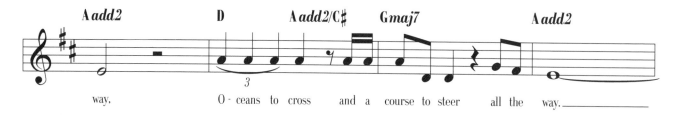

way, O-ceans to cross and a course to steer all the way.___

___ We bought ___ To San-ti-a-go.___

All the way___ to San-ti-a___ go. All the way___

G

to San - ti - a — go. All the way to San - ti - a —

G **Aadd2** **Bmin** **G** **D.S.** **al segno** **D** Fine

— go. All the way. And when the

Interlude **D** **G** **D** **G**

way, When Ma - ri - a y Juan y Ju - li - o, Fe - li - pe, Ped - ro y Ma - ri - o, I - sa -

D **G** **Aadd2** **G** **D.S. al fine**

bell - a y Man - uel, Mau - ri - cio Ven - ga - mos a la ca - sa a San - ti - a - go.

2.
We bought copper and ore, silver and gold,
From the mines and the fields the sweat of a people was sold,
Lights going down in the Barrios, a long day's labour at an end,
They saw the wealth of the mountains flow all the way to Santiago.

3.
And when the country was torn then we chose sides,
Selling arms to the few who could hold back the tide,
Fires burned in the Barrios and we poured oil upon the flames,
Sending bullets and bombs, guns and planes all the way...

4.
From the hearts of the west they'll fly back to the sun,
South America bound, the waiting is done,
There'll be laughter and songs in the Barrios to echo half the world away,

Interlude

Last chorus
All the way to Santiago (Juan y Maria y Mario),
All the way to Santiago (Isabella y Manuel),
All the way to Santiago,
All the way...

Short Stories outside the rehearsal
rooms in Maida Vale, 1982

Paul Downes and
I dressing up at
Bill Zorn's, 1981

Bill Zorn

John Bickford

Ligging in recording
studio, London, 1983

See My Baby Again

Words and music by Steve Knightley
From 'Backlog 1987-1991'

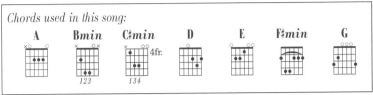

2.
Too long down the road, nowhere to put the load,
Only a bottle of wine keeping me sane,
It'll be alright when I see my baby again.

3.
Where's the 'phone? I gotta call, ringing the bell off the wall,
Coming off the road and out of the rain.
It'll be alright when I see my baby again.

Shadows In The Dark

Words and music by Steve Knightley
From 'Beat About The Bush'

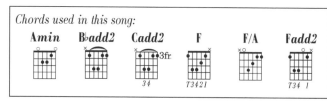

Moderato ♩ = 96

When he lost___ his way_____ at_____ twen_____ - _____ ty,_____

Shel - ter was___ - ___ n't hard_____ to find,_____ A

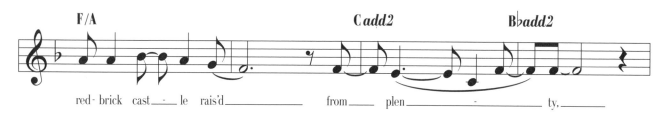

red - brick cast___ - ___ le rais'd_____ from_____ plen_____ - _____ ty,_____

When the wis_____ - ___ dom was,_____ "Bet - ter out_____ of sight___

___ and out___ of mind."_____

2.
Behind the walls he passed the seasons,
Never learnt the secrets of the town,
Now comes in this age of reason,
When the wisdom says:
"Unlock the door and close the castle down."

3.
By day amongst the shops and hallways,
At night he joins the sleepers in the park,
And in our crowded streets and doorways,
Where's the wisdom now,
That throws him like a shadow on the dark.

Silver Dagger

Traditional, arranged Knightley & Beer
From 'Show of Hands Live'

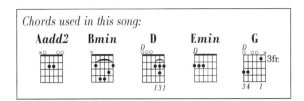

Chords used in this song:

Aadd2   Bmin   D   Emin   G

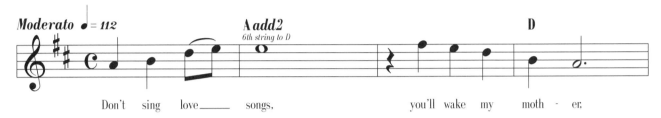

Don't sing love____ songs, you'll wake my moth - er,

She's sleep - ing here, right by my____ side,

And in her right hand, a sil - ver dag - ger,

She__ says that I can't__ be your bride____

2.
"All men are false," says my mother,
"They'll tell you wicked, loving lies;
"The very next evening, they'll court another,
"Leaving you alone to pine and sigh."

3.
My daddy is a handsome devil,
He's got a chain five miles long;
And on every link a young heart dangles,
Of another girl he's loved and wronged.

4.
Go court another tender lady,
And hope that she will be your wife;
For I've been warned and I've decided,
To sleep alone all of my life.
All of my life.
All of my life.

Sit You Down

Words and music by Steve Knightley
From 'Show of Hands Live'

Chords used in this song:

A Bmin D Emin G

Andante ♩ = 92
Intro

You used to sing____ at the break of day,_____

Through long ho___urs the sun would-n't fade____ a - way.____

Your eyes were bright____ and your voice grew strong___ er,____

You could-n't stay____ at home____ an- y long- er,____ Now you search___ for the ones___

___ with the means___ to pay.____ ____ Sit you

down____ at the jour- ney's end,____ The day___ has

2.
Some of us have never left this town,
We looked around a while and settled down,
Build our lives with those around us,
You left before you really found us,
But if the dreams you weave ever come unwound...
Chorus

3.
You walk with those that barely know your name,
And the sea of talking faces sounds the same,
Don't live and laugh with strangers too long,
Turn your steps back where you came from,
You left an empty space and it still remains.
Chorus.

Six O'Clock Waltz

Words and music by Steve Knightley
From 'Show of Hands Live'

Chords used in this song:

A   Dmaj7   E9   F#min7(sus4)   G

Allegro ♩ = 146

Verse (3rd verse) 8va

E9

It's dark in the morn - ing when the clock rings a

(8va)

F#min7(sus4)

warn - ing, I stum - ble down the hall - way and a

E9

Last time D.S. %

cold sun is dawn - ing. At six o'- clock,

six o'- clock...

Chorus   **A**   **Dmaj7**   **A**   **Dmaj7**

If I could lie 'til the far side of morn - ing I would,

A   **Dmaj7**   **A**

I'd stum - ble down dreams, lay 'til my bo - dy felt good,

G   **E9**

But it's six o'- clock, I'll do the six o'- clock

waltz...

D.C.

(Spoken) Or eight, or nine, or ten, or

twelve, or one - thir - ty... it's

**Repeat chorus
twice then to coda**

six o' - clock,_____ six o' - clock..._____

Coda

rit.

Wake up

2.
Look like death in the mirror where a pale face is staring;
I feel like a victim but I'm almost past caring,
At six o'clock, six o'clock...

3.
The radio's calling, it lies and it teases;
If the DJ starts joking I'm going to smash it to pieces,
At six o'clock, six o'clock...

4.
Don't feel like eating, my bed was like heaven;
Can't go on meeting myself before seven,
Or eight, or nine, or ten, or twelve, or one-thirty...
It's six o'clock, six o'clock.

Solo

Words and music by Steve Knightley
From 'Backlog 1987-1991'

Chords used in this song:

Aadd2 Amin C Cadd2 Dsus4 Fadd2 G

Andante ♩ = 88

Amin Aadd2 Cadd2 Dsus4 Amin

1. Since you've left I sleep a - lone, This
2. days a - head like step - ping stones, Of
3. *Instrumental*

Cadd2 Dsus4 Amin

emp - ty heart now feels like home, Where
dis - tan - ces be - tween us grown, I'm
Your

G Fadd2

sha - dows walk and dark - ness flows,
reach - ing out so let me know,
eyes re - veal what your heart can't show,

𝄋 C G Aadd2 Amin

To Coda ⊕

(2.) Dal segno 𝄋 al capo e poi la coda

(Why) You took me so high and left me so lo. The

Coda

⊕

C

—— lo You took me so

G Amin

high and left me so lo.

Tall Ships

Words and music by Steve Knightley
From 'Backlog 1987-1991'

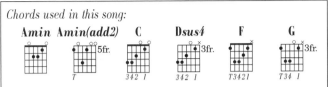

Chords used in this song:

(Refrain:) On the sky-line the tall ships sail by, Bound for Lon-don, their decks pil'd high; Fruits of warm-er lands, Pass-ing through our hands, So we look for a storm in the sky.

1.
Oh, the fishermen rise with the sun,
And they work 'til the day's nearly done;
Hauling empty nets while the cold sun sets,
And the winter is barely begun.
Refrain

2.
We have families with sons on the sea,
They work the tall ships of the sea;
But our choice is made by these winter's days,
And the children who watch from the quay.
Refrain

3.
November wind chills to the bone,
And December rain lashes the stones;
Sea that brings us life, take your sacrifice,
And give back the hope to our homes.
Refrain

4.
There's a lighthouse a mile from the shore,
That the storm-weary sailors search for;
When the wind and rain bring their gales again,
It won't shine for them any more.
Refrain

5.
As the rain-blackened clouds gather round,
And the roaring gales drown every sound,
All eyes search the night for that ray of light,
That warns where the black rocks are found.
Refrain

6.
That wild evening, the word flew around,
A tall merchant-man's tempted aground;
How we shout and sing, glad to greet the spring,
Though we weep for the sailors we've drowned.
Refrain

Unlock Me

Words and music by Steve Knightley
From 'Lie Of The Land'

Weary

Words and music by Steve Knightley
From 'Lie Of The Land'

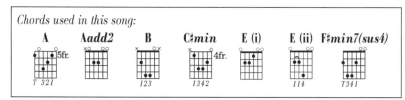

Chords used in this song:
A   Aadd2   B   C#min   E (i)   E (ii)   F#min7(sus4)

Andante ♩ = 80

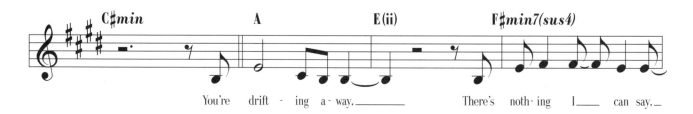

You're drift-ing a-way,_____ There's noth-ing I____ can say,__

_____ You're wea-ry,_____ You've

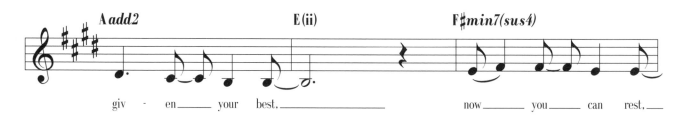

giv-en____ your best,_____ now_____ you____ can rest,__

_____ You're wea-ry,_____

Sleep   by the road_____   and the   night   will un-fold,_____   Soon_____

The Well

Words and music by Steve Knightley
From 'Lie Of The Land'

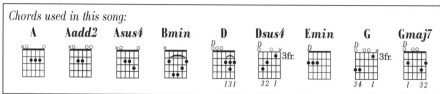

Chords used in this song:
A Aadd2 Asus4 Bmin D Dsus4 Emin G Gmaj7

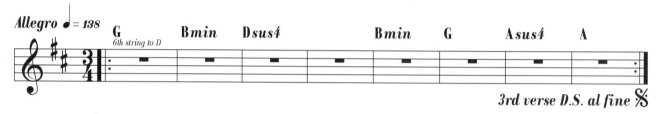

Allegro ♩ = 138

3rd verse D.S. al fine 𝄋

For - ty long days of sun beat - ing down, Hill - side the

col - our of rust, The grass in the fields_____

with- er'd and brown, A coun-try-side chok-ing in dust,

"Oh, I am your man,_____ I'll find you wat_____- er

deep un- der- ground,_____ Leave me a- lone_____ to walk on your land,_

I will ent - er my dream,   _As the ha - zel wand_

turns and twists in my hands, A hun - dred feet o - ver a

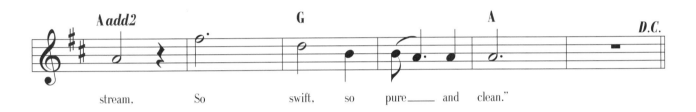

_stream, So swift, so pure___ and clean."_

2.
As the drill bore deep in the ground,
They held one another and stared,
The roaring grew louder, a fountain of sound,
Rose fifty feet in the air,
Now there's water enough to slake the dry throats,
Of the streams and the wells,
I took my fee, I left these words:
"Never question its worth,
"Let it pass through you to nourish and grow,
"And let it return to the Earth:
Who tries to possess it is cursed."

3.
"It will not be bought, bartered or sold,
"Traded like iron or coal,
"Those who seize water like silver and gold,
"Will only find ice in their soul—
"A desert where nothing will grow."

Well-Bred Clowns

Words and music by Steve Knightley
From 'Backlog 1987-1991'

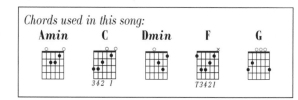

Chords used in this song:

Moderato ♩ = 96

Intro

I rose with the morn——ing on a rain——wash'd

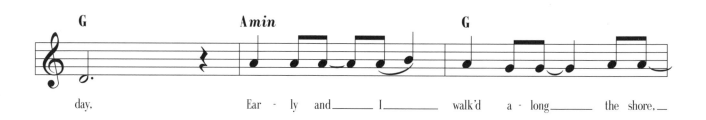

day, Ear - ly and—— I—— walk'd a - long—— the shore,—

Watch - ing the bro——ken, splin- ter'd

drift- wood—— com - ing in,—— I list - en'd to—— the

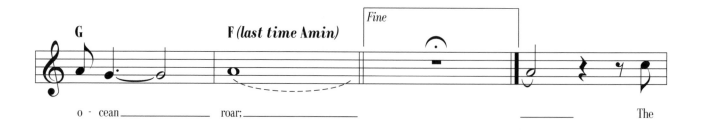

o - cean—— roar;—— The

town slow-ly wak-ing and I walk'd from the sea,____ Par-ents break in-to their chil-dren's____

____ dreams,_____ Moth-ers start to call, fath-ers reach the stir-ring streets,_____ And

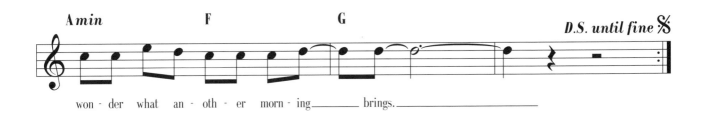

D.S. until fine 𝄋

won-der what an-oth-er morn-ing_____ brings._____

2.
All they have to sell is the strength of two strong arms,
All they own, standing in their shoes,
And the price of your labour, in deep winter it falls and falls,
The point came, there was nothing left to lose;
We paid the price of winter and we buy another year,
It's time to search the heart and count the cost,
Take the guilty conscience and the widow's bitter tear,
And what we gain is someone else's loss.

3.
Yesterday, the gales that shook the roof-top slates,
Today, the breeze gently turns your hair,
And the tide that closed its fist and snapped a broad ship's back,
Now softly takes the white gulls from the air;
Oh, the banker's purse is like a deep black well,
For every other well-bred clown,
And the merchant has a fleet full of young men's lives,
He can risk one in twenty going down.

4.
I rose with the morning on a rain-washed day,
It was early and I walked along the shore,
I knelt down by the water where my brother lay,
I listened to the ocean roar.

White Tribes

Words and music by Steve Knightley and Matt Clifford
From 'Beat About The Bush'

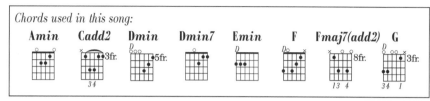

Andante ♩ = 84

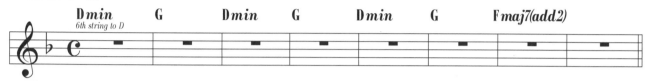

My ___ love, the bor ___ der's rest ___ less, Ru-mours be-ing ___ spread, ___

We learn ___ to speak in whis-pers, Leave so much ___ un-said; ___

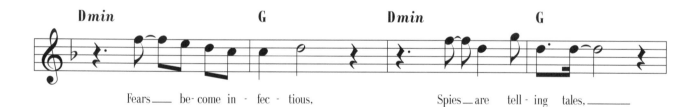

Fears ___ be-come in-fec-tious, Spies ___ are tell-ing tales, ___

There's strang ___ ers in the moun-tains, And scouts out on the trails; ___ The

walls of peace ___ were on ___ ly ___ pap ___ er thin, I can feel those shapes be-neath my ___

skin, The gen-er-a-tions drum in my head,_____ And the tribe a-wakes,_____

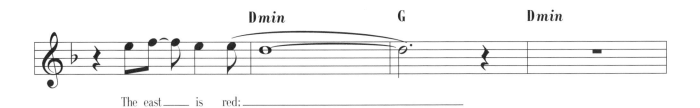

The east_____ is red;_____

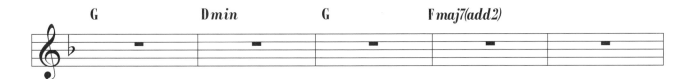

Cen-tur-ies of feud-ing_____ were on - ly held_____ in check,_____ When

war - lords have com-put _____ - ers_____ and ties a-round_____ their necks;_____

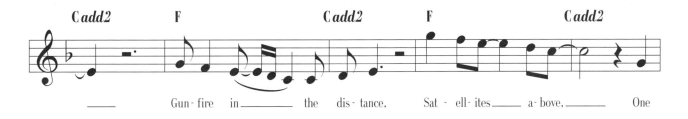

_____ Gun - fire in_____ the dis-tance, Sat-ell-ites_____ a-bove,_____ One

day when this is o - ver,_____ We'll meet a - gain,_____ my love._____

83

Winter's Welcome

Words and music by Steve Knightley
From 'Backlog 1987-1991'

I'm home - ward bound.

Verses 2 & 3

With the first clear sight____ of the West Count - ry shore,_____

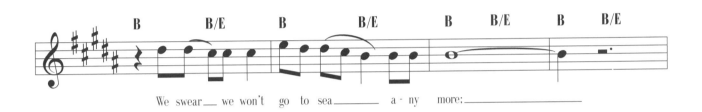

We swear___ we won't go to sea_____ a - ny more:_____

Sweet- hearts___ and wives_____ seem dear - er, As the Eng - lish shore_

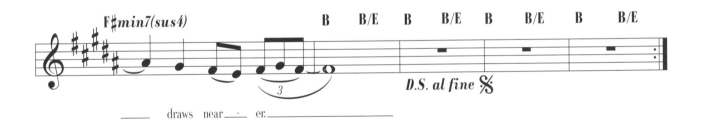

F#min7(sus4)

D.S. al fine

____ draws near__ - er._____

3.
Now soon, their welcome will warm a winter's heart,
We'll vow nothing will pull us apart;
There'll be a short time of plenty,
We'll think again when our pockets are empty.

4.
Now a grey cloud blackens the clear western skies,
Fear and welcome join both in our eyes;
Full sail and a straining main-mast,
Run with the wind, we'll fly while the storm lasts.
While the storm lasts.
I'm homeward bound.
I'm homeward bound.

© 1996 Isis Publishing and Dave Mallinson Publications

Wolf At The Door

Words and music by Steve Knightley
From 'Show of Hands Live'

There's some-thing mov _ ing in _ the trees. _ Saw a sha _ dow, _ I heard him breathe. _ Got to keep the wolf from my door, I think I know what he wants me for, I shook his hand and I found _ a claw, I saw him smile, now I've seen his jaws, And he keeps go _ _ ing

Got to keep the wolf from _ my door.

2.
But who, who let me buy just what I like?
And who, said everything will turn out right?
Now he's marching through the town,
Counts to three, he wants to blow the house down;
Says he's going to take the car,
Let him try, he won't get far.

The Monmouth re-enactment,
Topsham 1985, with John
Bickford and Paul Downes

An early **Show of Hands** photo
taken in Corscombe, Dorset, 1987

John Bickford

Nels Israelson

A shot from the **Alianza** photo
sessions, Gloucester 1992

Yankee Clipper

Traditional, arranged Knightley & Beer
From 'Show of Hands Live'

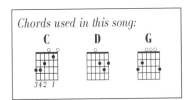

Chords used in this song:

C   D   G

342 1

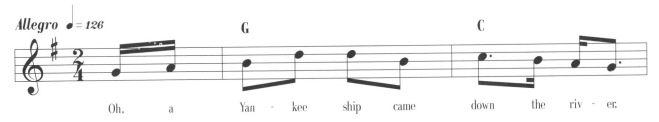

Oh, a Yankee ship came down the river,

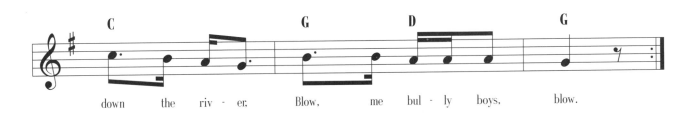

Blow, boys, blow, Oh, a Yankee ship came

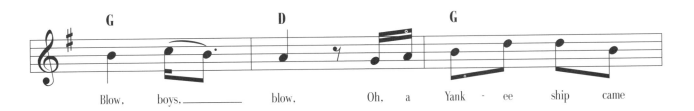

down the river, Blow, me bully boys, blow.

1.
Oh, a Yankee ship came down the river,
Blow, boys, blow,
Oh, a Yankee ship came down the river,
Blow, me bully boys, blow.
And how do you know she's a Yankee clipper?
Blow, boys, blow,
Her masts and yards shine like silver,
Blow, me bully boys, blow.

2.
This Yankee ship she's bound for China,
Blow, boys, blow,
Hurrah, me lads, let's go and join her,
Blow, me bully boys, blow.
This Yankee ship she's bound for China,
Blow, boys, blow,
Hurrah, me lads, let's go and join her,
Blow, me bully boys, blow.

3.
And who do you think's the captain of her?
Blow, boys, blow,
It's Randy Jack, the dancing sailor,
Blow, me bully boys, blow.
And who do you think's the captain of her?
Blow, boys, blow,
It's Randy Jack, the dancing sailor,
Blow, me bully boys, blow.

4.
And what do you think's the cargo of her?
Blow, boys, blow,
She's loaded all away with silver,
Blow, me bully boys, blow.
And what do you think's the cargo of her?
Blow, boys, blow,
She's loaded all away with silver,
Blow, me bully boys, blow.

Notes on the songs

Ah So!

Ah So! was written in 1986 and released on *Show of Hands'* first cassette. The basic premise of the song was that the economic miracle witnessed by Germany and Japan was related to the destruction of their industries and cities. Perhaps there was a cunning plan afoot to achieve the same result here! The irony seems a bit dated now and *Ah So!* is not a song currently in my repertoire.

All Your Fault

In 1991 when Phil and I began playing in bars and pubs we were short of up-tempo 'frothy' songs. *All Your Fault* was based musically on Dylan's *Si tu dois partir* and lyrically stems from an incident in the Marshwood Vale in Dorset when I drunkenly parked my car in a ditch and walked home, unable to accept responsibility for my own stupidity.

Armadas

The melody and the chord sequence are very much a result of my South American musical connections. The coincidence of all three leaders' names beginning with the letter 'M' seemed too good to ignore. The recorded version on *Beat about the Bush* is memorable for the vocal and instrumental contribution of actor and musician Vladimir Vega.

Beat About The Bush

Based upon a true story of a songwriter acquaintance who moved to London to find fortune and fame and ended up selling insurance to his friends. Incidentally, the time scale at the end of the song is just about right.

The Blind Fiddler

An American traditional folk song that Phil learnt from the playing of Dan Hartman. It remains one of *Show of Hands'* most requested songs.

The Blue Cockade

Collected in Beaminster in 1906. I have reorganised the lyrics to make (for me) better narrative sense. This is probably the most requested number in our repertoire and illustrates the beauty that can be created when a community recounts, through its singers and storytellers, its own experiences. The song is imbued with what Martin Carthy has called *'that most beautiful and precarious of emotions—resignation'*.

Bonnie Light Horseman

I first heard Polly Bolton singing this song in 1990 and actually learnt it during the Gulf War. I can remember watching television with the sound turned down and playing her cassette in the background. The contemporary images of conflict on screen combined with the melody and lyrics from the Napoleonic war were haunting.

Captains

Jerry Page, who promotes concerts in Mid-Sussex, is also a long-haul airline pilot; one night he spoke of his hope that someday he could look back on his career and consider all the thousands of people that he had brought safely home. It was an image that stayed with me and *Captains* was written a year later. On *Lie of the Land* I have set the song in Fleet, Hampshire—always the first stopping point on a journey from London to the West.

Cars

Playing in pubs and bars makes it necessary to develop certain survival strategies, the twelve-bar blues sequence being the most obvious. The challenge is to insert original material into the evening's set and persuade the crowd that they are in fact listening to the standards they expect! The line 'blasting through the chalk' refers to the destruction of Twyford Down in Hampshire, where the desecration of a landscape enables us all to arrive in Southampton ten minutes earlier.

Caught In The Rain

In 1991 keyboard player and friend Matt Clifford gave me a tape with half-a-dozen chord sequences on it. One in particular stood out. I played it over and over again in the car, developing melody lines and lyrics until, after a year or so, *Caught In The Rain* was completely written in my head. The version with Polly Bolton was recorded after less than ten minutes' rehearsal, immediately before the *Live* album was recorded.

Class Of Seventy-Three

I met a barman in Glasgow who had recently lost his job at the nearby steelworks. He told me that all his former friends and work-mates were either engaged in part-time work or had left home. Although this song is about coal mining, it could equally as well refer to any of our former manufacturing industries.

Notes on the songs

Columbus (Didn't Find America)
Written in 1992 during the Columbus 'celebrations', this was *Show of Hands'* first— and so far only—single. Disastrous timing saw it actually released a full year too late in January 1993...we didn't sell that many.

Day Has Come
Some dreams are so vivid that their flavour stays with you throughout the next day and leaves you with an almost tangible sense of a person or a place.

Don't It Feel Good
Anyone who frequented the London pub-rock scene in the early eighties may have caught *Short Stories* playing a fast and furious version of this song. It's the only one to have survived from those days and was one of the first songs that Phil and I began performing together.

Exile
In 1984 I was teaching guitar in a comprehensive school in Swiss Cottage. At that time there were a number of Ethiopian children newly arrived from Africa and I found both their dignity and displacement very moving. It then seemed that everywhere I looked in London there were South Africans, Poles, South Americans, Palestinians—the list is endless— unable to return home. The song was given a new lease of life by Kate Rusby and Katherine Roberts.

Friends
There used to be a folk club in the Double Locks Hotel on the canal banks in Exeter. Coming home after a long absence it was always possible to find old friends there and the memory of those Saturday nights is still vivid. There is constant talk of a reunion and maybe this will happen one day.

The Galway Farmer
Knowing the Cheltenham and Gloucester area well, I had heard lots of stories about the annual Irish invasion and this song contains aspects of some of them. At the time of writing it, I found myself playing the album *Hung up and Dry* by *Afterhours* and I live in hope that one day I can persuade Messrs Burke, Potts and co. to learn the damn song.

The Hook Of Love
One of only a couple of fingerpicking songs that I have written, the occasional request for this song is usually very forceful and insistent. Someone accused me once of having read their diaries.

The Hunter
Contrary to first impressions, this is not an anti-hunting song: it is saying "no" to the notion that to be human is to be a predator and that the laws of the jungle and the market are universal truths.

I'll Put A Stake Through His Heart
This song was born during a song-writing 'workshop' at the Wimborne Festival in 1992. Mike Silver and I were put into a room with a handful of would-be singer-songwriters and a load of morris men driven indoors by the rain. The afternoon passed with reasonable success and it was subsequently very amusing to receive a written request for *Steak In His Heart* at a concert in the Midlands.

I Still Wait
It was once suggested to me that if I could write a 'country' ballad I could make a lot of money from cover versions. Well, cowboys, here it is...and I'm still here as well.

The Keeper
July 1st, 1916 - the first morning of the Battle of the Somme and perhaps the most tragic morning in British military history. The Devonshire Regiment, in particular, suffered devastating losses. I have always been suspicious of songs that portray soldiers as naïve innocents, mere victims of the system. The keeper in this song is aware of his situation and even takes a degree of pride in his skills.

The Last Picture Show
Written in 1978 and another song about small town life, this time set in Texas. Peter Bogdanovich's film made a strong impression on me when I saw it in the late '70s.

Lovers, Never Friends
Lots of chords in this one. A song not really typical of my material and one that has never had a public outing. However, I still agree with the general sentiment that without a clean break, things cannot mend. I have seen too many 'we're still good friends' couples where at least one of the parties is desperate for reconciliation and the real conflict is only just beginning.

Low Down In The Broome
Paul Downes and I have been performing this number ever since we were at school together. The classical guitar arrangement of the song is from John Duarte's *English Suite*.

Continued overleaf

Notes on the songs

The Man In Green
Written in 1985 to celebrate the Duke of Monmouth's visit to Topsham that launched the ill-fated rebellion. Many Westcountrymen flocked to his green banner seeing him as a force of nature and an embodiment of the ancient 'green man' myths. The song was sung from the window of the actual room in the inn where he stayed.

Man Of War
I heard a story about a Dorset farmer who divided his farm between four sons, none of whom could make a living on their portion of land. All of them left the county and now only the ruined farmhouse remains. I have heard that *Man Of War* is being widely sung around the clubs and *The Albion Band*'s version on *Acousticity* is a memorable one.

Nine Hundred Miles/Poor Wayfaring Stranger
Two American folk songs welded together on *Beat About The Bush*, both about travelling and trains. Widely sung in England since the early days of the folk revival and borrowed from the playing of Davey Graham, amongst others.

The Oak
In 1991 Morna Watson, director of *The Theatre of the Heart*, asked me to write a song for a 'tree-dressing' ceremony in Beaminster, west Dorset. Hundreds of local people gathered around a suitably dressed hollow oak at sunset on a cold December's afternoon. The chorus was originally intended to be sung as a round.

The Preacher
In the American tradition there is a well-documented association of sex with death. This song is set in the rather 'Gothic' landscape of Portland and attempts to relocate an American 'frailing banjo'-style folk song in Dorset.

Ratcliffe Highway
A traditional song in which a West Country sailor literally overturns the tables whilst ashore in London. This version was learnt from Exeter singer Paul Downes who found it in the *Penguin Book Of English Folk Songs*—still for me the finest collection of traditional English material ever published.

Safe As Houses
Staying with friends in South Norwood, I became aware of just how security-conscious one must be in order to safeguard what every Englishman once called his 'castle'.

Santiago
Phil and I were introduced to exiled Chilean musicians Mauricio Venegas, Vladimir Vega and Sergio Avila in 1991. Roger Watson of Bracknell-based *TAPS* (Traditional Arts Projects) had managed to secure funding for an Anglo-Chilean musical collaboration and with Dave Townsend of *The Mellstock Band*, *Alianza* was formed. We recorded an album and toured extensively throughout 1992 and 1993.

See My Baby Again
A touch of 'folkabilly' written in 1980 and played a great deal by *Arizona Smoke Review*. Still popular, especially when linked with the ridiculous 'Elvis comes to Teignmouth' anecdote!

Shadows In The Dark
There used to be three vast Victorian mental institutions in East Devon, self-contained with their own orchards, nurseries and sports facilities. Phil Beer's father was in fact the chief administrator of the largest of them, Exminster. Now they are all closed and those who would have formerly become inmates are being cared for 'in the community'. For some it seems, sadly, that 'in the community' means on the streets.

Silver Dagger
I first heard this song being sung by Joan Baez on one of her early recordings and I have been singing it since I was sixteen. However, it is only recently that the inner meaning of the song has become apparent to me. The girl's mother is not protecting her daughter from the lover outside the house but from the man within. This realisation has transformed an excellent song into something that I now find dark and disturbing.

Sit You Down
This song is about the leaving of small towns in general and Exmouth in particular. It's still my mum's favourite!

Six O'Clock Waltz
When I was as student I found summer work on the motorway near Exeter. This entailed getting up at six in order to clock on at the site at eight. Everyone said that I would get used to early rising; however, I found that I would still be wide awake at two in the morning. Whenever I am asked if intensive touring is tiring I always reply (without joking) that nothing a musician may do is as exhausting as a *real* job.

Solo
A song rarely played these days. One of Mike Silver's favourites and so probably worth reviving next time I see him.

Notes on the songs

Tall Ships

Widely requested and in some areas believed to be a traditional song, *Tall Ships* was first performed in the Brighton area in the late '70s by myself and double bass player Warwick Downes. The story is set in a small West Country fishing village just after the Napoleonic Wars. The catch is meagre and the harvest fails. The villagers, in desperation, decide to wreck a passing merchantman by placing a false light on the cliffs and tempting it onto the rocks. They succeed but among the drowned sailors they discover the body of a young man born and raised in the village. He had gone to sea a year before and was serving on board of the unfortunate ship. I have broken the complete *Tall Ships* piece into its three main component songs, *Winter's Welcome*, *Well-Bred Clowns* and, of course, *Tall Ships*; these notes refer to all three songs.

Unlock Me

A song about 'false memory syndrome' and the dangers of entering into an economic relationship with another person who then has a vested interest in uncovering events in the past which may have never occurred.

Weary

A spell to bring peace and rest.

The Well

Written during the drought of 1995. A water dowser agrees to find water on condition that it is not subsequently owned or sold.

Well-Bred Clowns

See *Tall Ships*.

White Tribes

Another song constructed from one of Matt Clifford's piano sequences. The title comes from the television documentary *The White Tribes Of Africa*. In this instance I had in mind the conflict in the former Yugoslavia.

Winter's Welcome

See *Tall Ships*.

Wolf At The Door

Keyboard player Matt Clifford has worked with some illustrious names in the music world. One day, having just flown in from Mustique, he met Phil and I on our way to Wolverhampton. "Still," he said "it keeps the wolf from the door." We agreed to have a race to see who could write a song with that title the quickest—I won. (I have nothing against Wolverhampton, by the way.)

Yankee Clipper

A 'Cajun' sea shanty...often requested, seldom played.

Performing at *Theatre of the Heart's* 'The Oak', Beaminster, Dorset, 1991

George Wright

Rob O'Connor

Live recording session: ***Show of Hands*** at The Bull, Bridport, June 1992, showing (left to right) Mike Silver, Phil Beer, myself, Polly Bolton, Paul Downes and Matt Clifford

George Wright

With Phil and Jack the dog, at Wytherston Studios, Dorset 1994

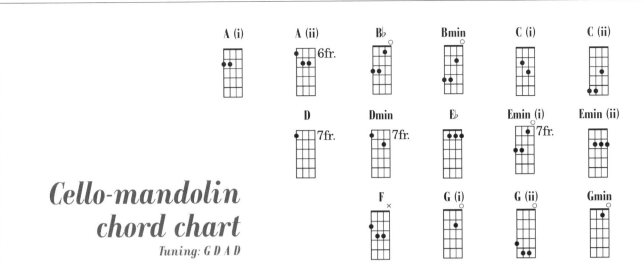

A (i)	A (ii)	B♭	Bmin	C (i)	C (ii)

D	Dmin	E♭	Emin (i)	Emin (ii)

Cello-mandolin chord chart

Tuning: G D A D

F	G (i)	G (ii)	Gmin

Cambridge Festival 1993

Steve Weaver

Show Of Hands - Discography

Lie Of The Land
Isis IS09 1995
Captains
Exile
The Hunter
The Keeper
The Man In Green
M Ferguson
The Preacher
Ratcliffe Highway
Safe As Houses
Unlock Me
Weary
The Well

Beat About The Bush
Isis IS05 1994
Armadas
Beat About The Bush
The Blue Cockade
Cars
Class Of Seventy-Three
Day Has Come
The Galway Farmer
The Hook Of Love
Mr May's/The Gloucester
Hornpipe
Nine Hundred Miles/Poor
Wayfaring Stranger
The Oak
Shadows In The Dark
White Tribes

Show Of Hands Live
Isis IS06 1994
All Your Fault
The Blind Fiddler
Bonnie Light Horseman
Caught In The Rain
Don't It Feel Good
Exile
I'll Put A Stake Through His
Heart
I Still Wait
Low Down In The Broome
Man Of War
Santiago
Silver Dagger
Sit You Down
Six O'Clock Waltz
Wolf At The Door
Yankee Clipper

Backlog 1987 - 1991
Isis IS08 1995
Ah So!
The Dominion Of The Sword
First They Take Manhattan
Friends
Homes For Heroes
The Last Picture Show
The Leaving Blues
Limbo
Lovers, Never Friends
The Pleasures Of The
Town/The Seneca Two-Step
See My Baby Again
Solo
Tall Ships/Well-Bred
Clowns/Winter's Welcome
The Tramp Stamp/Chasing
The Jack
Walking In The Rain

**Columbus (Didn't
Find America)**
Isis IS07 1994
Breakfast For Altan
Columbus (Didn't Find
America)
Exile
Scattering Tears